CALAMITY JANE

A MUSICAL WESTERN

adapted by

RONALD HANMER *and* PHIL PARK

from

the stage play

by

CHARLES K. FREEMAN

after

The WARNER BROS. Film

written by

JAMES O'HANLON

Lyrics *Music*

by *by*

PAUL FRANCIS WEBSTER SAMMY FAIN

Vocal Score

© 2006 by Faber Music Ltd
First published by International Music Publications Ltd
International Music Publications Ltd is a Faber Music company
3 Queen Square, London WC1N 3AU
Printed in England by Caligraving Ltd
All rights reserved

ISBN10: 0-571-52792-2
EAN13: 978-0-571-52792-2

To buy Faber Music publications or to find out about the full range of titles available,
please contact your local music retailer or Faber Music sales enquiries:

Faber Music Ltd, Burnt Mill, Elizabeth Way, Harlow, CM20 2HX England
Tel: +44(0)1279 82 89 82   Fax: +44(0)1279 82 89 83
sales@fabermusic.com   fabermusic.com

CALAMITY JANE

CHARACTERS

CALAMITY JANE	*The hard-bitten, gun-totin' heroine, who tries to behave like a man but can't help loving like a woman*
WILD BILL HICKOCK	*Handsome, professional gambler, about 35*
LIEUT. DANNY GILMARTIN	*Good-looking young officer*
KATIE BROWN	*Attractive stage-struck young lady from the Big City*
HENRY MILLER	*Proprietor of " The Golden Garter "*
SUSAN	*Miller's pretty young niece*
FRANCIS FRYER	*A song-and-dance man*
ADELAIDE ADAMS	*A show-business star*
RATTLESNAKE	*An old stage-coach driver*
" DOC " PIERCE	*Deadwood's doctor-undertaker*
JOE	*Bartender at " The Golden Garter "*
HANK } PETE }	*Two Scouts*
THE COLONEL OF FORT SCULLY	

COWPUNCHERS, BULLWHACKERS, PROSPECTORS, TRAPPERS, INDIANS, WOMEN OF THE TOWN, CHORUS-GIRLS, OFFICERS, SOLDIERS and their WIVES, STAGE-COACH PASSENGERS, ETC.

SYNOPSIS OF SCENES

ACT ONE

SCENE 1   " THE GOLDEN GARTER ", Deadwood City, Dakota Territory
SCENE 2   THE STAR DRESSING-ROOM, Bijou Theatre, Chicago
SCENE 3   " THE GOLDEN GARTER " again

ACT TWO

SCENE 1   CALAMITY JANE'S CABIN
SCENE 2   A TRAIL, through a Pass in the Black Hills
SCENE 3   FORT SCULLY
SCENE 4   THE TRAIL again
SCENE 5   " THE GOLDEN GARTER "

Time : 1876

CALAMITY JANE

NOTES ON PRINCIPAL CHARACTERS

CALAMITY JANE—In order to hold her own in a man's world, she dresses, speaks, rides and shoots like a man; groomed and dressed in proper feminine fashion, she is revealed as a beautiful girl—and the transformation is quite startling.

WILD BILL HICKOCK—Aged about 35, and a handsome figure of a man, he is an ex-peace-officer turned professional gambler. Good-natured, with a sense of humour. In love with Calamity Jane, but doesn't know it.

LIEUT. DANNY GILMARTIN—A young officer attached to the nearby fort. He is the man Calamity Jane dreams about, but he falls in love with somebody quite different.

KATIE BROWN—A stage-struck city-girl who poses as a famous actress, but has good looks and talents of her own.

HENRY MILLER—Proprietor of "The Golden Garter" Deadwood City's saloon-hotel-theatre. Aged about 50, he is nervous and erratic, giving the impression he is constantly only one jump ahead of a nervous breakdown. (Non-Singing)

SUSAN—Miller's young, friendly and pretty niece. (Non-Singing).

FRANCIS FRYER—A song-and-dance man more at home in the vaudeville theatres of the Eastern States than in the Wild West.

ADELAIDE ADAMS—A highly-paid vaudeville star and celebrated " beauty " of the period : off-stage, a selfish and conceited woman.

RATTLESNAKE—A bewhiskered old fossil who drives the stage-coach. (Non-Singing).

" DOC " PIERCE—Deadwood City's doctor-undertaker, with doubtful qualifications but considerable experience. A poker-playing pal of Hickock's. (Non-Singing).

JOE—Bartender at " The Golden Garter ". (Non-Singing).

THE ORCHESTRA

The complete orchestra for " Calamity Jane " comprises, 3 Trumpets, 2 Trombones, 4 Saxes, Horn, Violins A. B. C., Viola, Cello, Bass, Guitar, Drums and Piano. The 1st Alto, 2nd Alto and 2nd Tenor Saxes double Clarinet; the 1st Tenor Sax doubles Flute. However, in the event of Saxes not being available, parts are provided for non-doubling Flute and 1st and 2nd Clarinets. A 3rd Clarinet may be added by playing the whole of the 2nd Tenor Sax part on Clarinet. A special orchestral piano part is supplied, which should be used ; the pianist should NOT use the vocal score. The Violin parts are printed Violin A to one book ; Violin B and C together in a second book.

The minimum combination for a successful performance is 2 Trumpets, 1 Trombone, 3 Saxes (or 3 Wood-wind), 3 Violins, Cello, Bass, Drums and Piano. Thereafter, instruments should be added in the following order ; 2nd Trombone, 2nd Tenor Sax (or 3rd Clarinet), 3rd Trumpet, additional Violins, Viola, Horn and Guitar.

All parts are cued where necessary, and the vocal score has complete instrumental marks and cues for the conductors' guidance.

RONALD HANMER

CALAMITY JANE

MUSICAL NUMBERS

CALAMITY JANE

Lyrics by
PAUL FRANCIS WEBSTER

Music by
SAMMY FAIN
Music adapted
and arranged by
RONALD HANMER

OVERTURE

4

ACT I

THE DEADWOOD STAGE
(CALAMITY and ENSEMBLE)

8

Cho. Oh, the Deadwood Stage is a headin' on ov-er the hills ___ where the

Cho. In - jun arrows are a - thicker than porkerpine quills ___ Dangerous land ___

Cho. No time to de - lay ___ Whipcrack a - way, whip crack a - way, whipcrack a -

THREE OR FOUR MEN

They're head-in' straight for town load-ed down with a fan - cy

Cho way! ___

9

Cho. Whip crack a-way, whip crack a-way, whip crack a- way! _____

Cho. Here they be! Here they be! How's a-bout a wel-come? A peace - ful sort of welcome for the

Cho. gang! Bang! Oh, the Deadwood stage is finall - y home a - gain!

CALAMITY JANE enters followed by RATTLESNAKE and passengers from the stage - coach

CARELESS WITH THE TRUTH
(CALAMITY, BILL & MEN)

Cue: CALAMITY: You callin' me a liar again Bill Hickock?
AD LIBS: Tell us another etc.

Cal.
I - da - ho come on to save the day _____ In honour of me the

L'istesso tempo (♩.=♩)

Cal.
Pres - i - dent put a buf - fa - lo on the nick - el and an In - jun on the cent ____

Stgs. Clar.

BILL
Tell us another one, tell us another one, oh, my ach - in'

TENORS

BARITONES
Ha, ha, ha, ha, ha, ha, ha, ha!

BARITONES

BASSES

TUTTI

Bill
tooth, She's not ex - act - ly ly - in', but she's care - less with the truth!

Brass

TUTTI

25

26

№ 3

ADELAIDE
(BILL & MEN)

Cue: BILL: You see her carved on the prow of an ancient ship. . . .
. . . . in a gambler's cameo . . . .
in the dyin' embers of a campfire . . . .

Moderato in 4 (♩ = 122)

In this case, she just happens to be the loveliest singin' dancin' star of them all . . . . Adelaide Adams!

If you gave a man a wish, ten to one he would wish for that one per-fect girl Ad-e-

-laide, Adelaide, Ad-el-aide, oh, how lovely you are!_____ If you gave a man a dream, ten to

Mm_____ love-ly! Ad-e-laide

Nº 4   EV'RYONE COMPLAINS ABOUT THE WEATHER

(FRYER)

Cue: FRYER: But you can at least let me *show* you! . .

Nº 5

MEN!

Cue: BILL: "Like a touchy old woman."...
H'm ... Maybe he's got something there ....
CALAMITY: Why, you ... you ...!
(She reaches for something to throw at him)
Men...!

Nº 6 CAN - CAN

Cue: MILLER: .... the Golden Garter Show!

HIVE FULL OF HONEY
(FRYER)

Cue; MILLER:...the toast of New York.... Miss Frances Fryer!

(FRYER *enters*) **Moderate 4 (♩=112)**

Tpt Solo

1

FRYER: (*In high-pitched girls falsetto*)

I've got two wonderful arms, I've got two wonderful lips, I'm ov-er

Vlns. W.W.

mp Cello

Fry. twen-ty one— and I'm free_____ Oh, I've got a hive full of hon-ey For the

Tpt. 3

Trom. Sust.

Fry. right kind of hon-ey bee!_____ I'm not the glam-or-ous type, but I'm the

Vlns. W.W.

f muted Br.

mp Cello

I CAN DO WITHOUT YOU

(CALAMITY and BILL)

№ 8

Cue: CALAMITY; ain't nuthin' you say means anything to me! . . . .

Moderate 2 (♩ = 88)

CALAMITY: In the summer, you're the win-ter In the fin-ger, you're the splinter! In the

banquet you're the stew – Say! I can do without you! In the gar-den, you're the

net-tle and the mil-dew on the pet-al! Like an ov-er-turned can-oe, Well!

BILL: I can do without you! You can go to Phil-a-del-phi-a take a hack to Hacken-

54

SEGUE Nº 9

Nº 9

Nº 10 "IT'S HARRY I'M PLANNING TO MARRY"

(ADELAIDE and the JOHNNIES)

Cue: ADELAIDE: . . . . my farewell performance!

58

Harry I'm plan-ning to mar-ry

Harry plan-ning to mar-ry

do

ff

№10a   REPRISE: "IT'S HARRY I'M PLANNING TO MARRY"

(KATIE)

Cue: KATIE strikes an 'Adelaide Adams' pose in front of mirror.

Valse moderato in 1 (♩= 60)

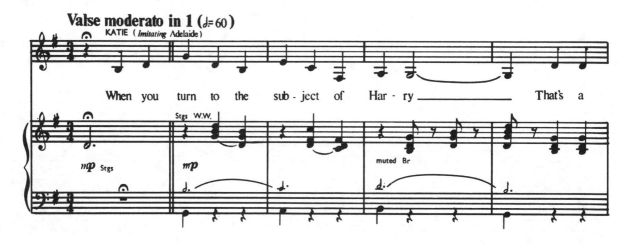

KATIE (Imitating Adelaide)

When you turn to the sub-ject of Har-ry _____ That's a

mp Stgs   Stgs W.W.   mp   muted Br

horse of a diff-'rent sa-far-i; _____ He can box like a

muted Br

mp Stgs. Cls.

Nᵒ 11   OPENING SCENE III

Reprise: ADELAIDE
(MEN)

Cue CALAMITY: . . . somebody's being hustled. *(Black-out)*

NOTE: If shorter scene-change music is required, the first repeat may be omitted, or a start made at either ① or ②

63

64

66

Men   —   Ad - el - aide,   Ad - el - aide,   Ad - el - aide,   Oh, how

Men   love - ly you are _____ Now that

7

Men   you have come to town   you can bet   all the town will be out

Nº 12

WINDY CITY
(CALAMITY & CHORUS)

Cue: CALAMITY: . . . . the biggest noise in Illinois!

70

Cal. all dressed up in a suit of yeller and the dance he did there, went something like

8 **Schottische** (*Soft shoe style* ♩ = 120)

Cal. this.

9

Nº 13

KEEP IT UNDER YOUR HAT
(KATIE)

Cue: MILLER: ....the one and only Adelaide Adams!

KATIE (very nervous and hesitant)

Well, now if you've got a cu-tie who's a real sweet patootie, bet-ter keep it under your hat—

Just re-mem-ber cu-ri-os-i-ty in fa-bles of old— killed the cur-i-ous cat—

(crowd starts to murmur, resentfully)

Suppos-in' you have a laddie who's a real sug-ar dad-dy, Bet-ter take in the welcoming mat—

Re-mem-ber there's a do-zen dolls for ev-ry Dan— You're not the on-ly sweet pea

Kate.

in the can;___ So if you wanna know theway to keep your man,___ Keep it un-der your

Kate.

hat, Hat-tie, Keep it under your hat, Hat-tie, Keep it under your hat!

Nº 14 REPRISE: KEEP IT UNDER YOUR HAT
(KATIE & CHORUS)

Cue: KATIE: My own way? Okay — I will!

Moderato 4 (♩ =120)
KATIE *(with style & confidence)*

Well,now if you've got a cu-tie Who's a real sweet patootie, Better

Kate

keep it un der your hat___ Just re-member cu-ri-os-i-ty, in fa-bles of old___

82

№ 15

FINALE ACT I
REPRISE: CARELESS WITH THE TRUTH
(ENSEMBLE & CHORUS)

Cue: CALAMITY: . . . .the only girl for the Golden Garter was *Katie Brown!*
(*Big laugh from everybody*)

Cho. not ex-act-ly ly-in', But she's care-less, care-less, care-less,

Tutti

mp *cresc.*

2

Cho. care-less — with the truth! _____

ff

Cho.

CURTAIN

END OF ACT I

№ 16   ENTR'ACTE

ACT II
OPENING ACT II
A WOMAN'S TOUCH
(CALAMITY & KATIE)

№ 17

90

Slower

Cal. rub-rub here, and a rub-rub there she can polish up the win-ders, Then pre-sto change-o sud-den-ly, the

Kate.

Tempo primo

Cal. sun comes peeping through "How-dy - do"

Kate. And what does Mister Sunshine say to you? It

Stgs. pizz. W.W. (Triangle)

mf

f Tutti

5

Cal

Kate makes you blink To stop and think A woman and a whisk-broom can ac-

W.W.

Stgs.

Cello

94

№ 18

HIGHER THAN A HAWK
(BILL)

Cue: **BILL**: *(looking at photo)* What a gal . . . .

Nº 19

BLACK HILLS OF DAKOTA
(CHORUS)

Cue: CALAMITY swoons into BILL'S arms. Blackout. Tabs.

102

Cho Black Hills of Da - ko - ta, to the beau - ti - ful In - di - an coun - try that I love_____

5

Cho _____ Mm_____ Mm_____ A - way_____

Black Hills, Black Hills, Though I've wandered far a - way

Cup Br Vlns. p

6

Cho Mm_____ Mm_____ Where the deer and the

Black Hills, Black Hills, I'll comeback to you some day!

Cl Fl

Stgs mf

(Tom –Tom)

108

Cho. love!_____ So take me, Take me back to the Black Hills, The

Cho Black Hills of Da - ko - ta_____ To the beau-ti-ful In-di-an coun-try that I love. Black

Cho Hills, I love! love! love!_____

Segue, after applause

№ 19a

OPENING SCENE III
REPRISE: BLACK HILLS OF DAKOTA
(CALAMITY, KATIE, BILL, DANNY & CHORUS.)

LOVE YOU DEARLY
(KATIE & DANNY)

Cue: **DANNY**: Calamity can be your bridesmaid . . . .

Nº 21

FINALETTO
(CALAMITY & BILL)

Cue. BILL: . . . . disrupt the whole fort if they see ya like that ! (Exit)

the way....

BILL: I'm takin' you home whether you like it or not - so c'mon -

CALAMITY: Now see here, Bill Hickock -

BILL: For Pete's sake let's get goin..... If anyone catches you an' me this way, Deadwood City'll never

be the same again! Exeunt. CURTAIN

6

ten ten

f Tutti

ff

ten ten

Segue as one

N⁰ 22 OPENING SCENE IV

Broadly (♩ = 80)

ff Tutti

CURTAIN UP *Enter* CALAMITY *and* BILL

Fl. Vlns.

Alto Sax (or Cl.)

Fade out on dialogue

Vln

rit

Nº 23   MY SECRET LOVE
(CALAMITY)

Cue: BILL: You'll get over Danny, too....

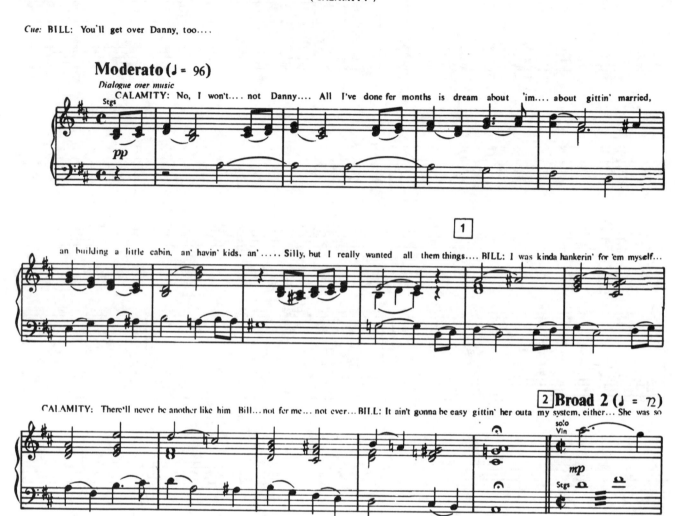

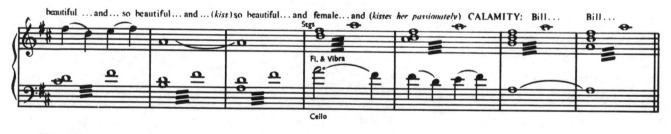

Cal.

Ev - en told the gol-den daf-fo-dils! At last my heart's an op-en

Moderate rhythm

Cal

door,_____ And my secret love's no secret, an-y more._____

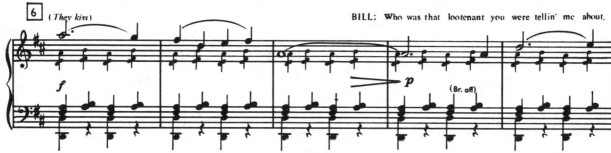

6 (They kiss)   BILL: Who was that lootenant you were tellin' me about,

a while back?   CALAMITY: Never heard of im... BILL: What you say to us takin' a ride just the two of us?

We could watch the moon hangin' high over the mountains.... CALAMITY: The way it'll look, I shan't ever have seen it before....

№ 23a MELOS AND REPRISE: MY SECRET LOVE
(CALAMITY & BILL)

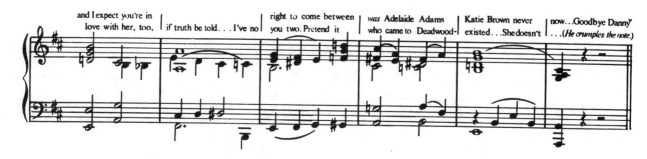

BILL   "Never existed" .... She was the most *real* person in Deadwood.

CALAMITY   *(with sudden resolution)* I've gotta bring her back .... There's nothin' else for it— I've gotta bring her back!

DANNY   But she's on her way to Valley Falls –

CALAMITY   But she ain't gonna catch no stage – not while I can ride faster'n any woman alive!   I'm gittin' back to the cabin, quick! Bill, you can saddle up fer me, while I get m'deerskins on .... While I'm gone, find a preacher to do the splicin'! .... Danny, you git back to the Fort an' invite the folks to a weddin'— a *double* weddin'— you and Katie, 'n me and Bill.

DANNY   *(after a stunned pause)* Did – did you say you – and--- Bill?

CALAMITY   That's right!

BILL   Sure is.

DANNY   Well I'll be! .... Bill, I don't know what kind of a life you'll have with this catamount, ...

Segue

REPRISE: WINDY CITY
(CHORUS)

Bright 2 (♩ = 108)

NOTE: If shorter scene-change music is required, the first repeat may be omitted, or a start made at either ☐1 or ☐2

Just blew in from the Win-dy Ci-ty, The Win-dy Ci-ty is migh - ty pretty, But they aint got what

№ 25

FINALE
(FULL COMPANY)

Cue: RATTLESNAKE: Deadwood Stage all ready fer the weddin' party!

CHORUS: Oh, the Deadwood stage is a-rol-lin' on ov-er the plains_____

Cho.: With the cur-tains flappin' and the driver a-slappin' the reins_____

Cho.: Beauti-ful sky_____ A won-der-ful day_____ Whip crack a-way, whip

Cho. crack a-way, Whip crack a - way! _____ Oh, the Deadwood Stage is a headin' on ov-er the

Cho. hills._____ Where the In - jun arrows are a - thicker than porkerpine quills_____

Cho. _ Dangerous land_____ no time to de - lay_____

3 L'istesso tempo

Cho. Whip crack a-way, Whip crack a-way, Whip crack a-way!

Enter SUSAN *in a Wedding Dress*   CHORUS GIRLS

A woman's touch!   A woman's touch!

Cho. The mag-ic of Al - ad-din could-n't do as much!   She's a

Cho. wiz - ard—she's a champ— and she does-n't need a lamp!

Cho. -thicker than porkerpine quills._____ Dangerous land,_____ No

Cho. time to de-lay._____ Whip crack a-way, whip crack a-way, whip crack a-

Cho. -way! Whip crack a - way!_____

Timps

CURTAIN

CURTAIN CALL
(THE BLACK HILLS OF DAKOTA)

PLAY - OUT

Timps.